WORDLE
CHALLENGE

for kids

© 2022 Quarto Publishing plc

First published in 2022 by words & pictures,
an imprint of The Quarto Group.
The Old Brewery, 6 Blundell Street,
London, N7 9BH, United Kingdom.
T (0)20 7700 6700 F (0)20 7700 8066
www.quarto.com

A catalogue record for this book is available from the British Library.

ISBN: 978-0-7112-8168-4

9 8 7 6 5 4 3 2 1

Compiled and designed by Tim Dedopulos and Roland Hall

Printed and bound by CPI Group (UK) Ltd, Croydon, CR0 4YY

FSC
www.fsc.org
MIX
Paper from
responsible sources
FSC® C171272

WORDLE
CHALLENGE
100 puzzles to do anywhere, anytime

for kids

words & pictures

CONTENTS

INTRODUCTION

Welcome to this book of challenging, new word puzzles. As you probably know, solving puzzles is good exercise for your brain. In the same way that your body is better off if it can run around and keep fit, your brain tends to work better if you keep it busy with interesting, challenging and stimulating exercise. Luckily, solving puzzles is also fun and can be done at any time of day, alone or with friends and family.

We created these puzzles for a little brain workout and to be fun at the same time. So get comfortable, sharpen your pencil and have a go at some of the puzzles inside the pages of this book. They do get harder as you progress, but you should be able to solve them all if you persevere – or ask for some help!

If you get really stuck I suggest you move on to another puzzle to clear the block, and come back later. It's amazing what a quick break or change will do for your solving skills.

Have fun!

HOW TO SOLVE

If you have encountered Wordle puzzles before, you will be familiar with the puzzles you find in this book. And if this is your first time Wordling, there's nothing to worry about – it's nice and easy!

You are trying to find a five-letter word by using the letter clues in the grid and the extra clue above each puzzle. The appearance of each letter tells you if it is in the solution word, and also where it appears.

A white letter on a black background tells you that the letter is in the solution and in the correct position, for example the letters **G**, **R** and **A** below:

A black letter on a grey background means the letter is in the solution but in the wrong position, for example the letters **G**, **A** and **R** below:

A black letter on a white background means that the letter is not in the solution at all, for example the letters **D**, **I** and **N** below:

The clue is FRUIT, so the solution to the puzzle is GRAPE:

Each puzzle has a letter marker underneath, so you can keep track of which letters have been ruled out, like this:

If you cross off the letters that you know are not in the word it will make finding the solution a bit easier.

One last thing to note: if a clue word in the grid has a double letter, (for example SHEEP), and the word you are looking for has one E, we will only mark the letter E once, the first time it appears. If there are two Es, we will mark both of them – it's an extra clue!

EASY

PUZZLES

Puzzle 1

Clue: seaside

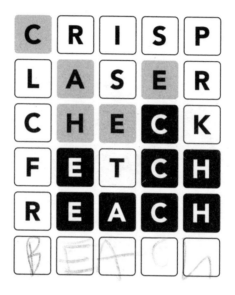

Puzzle 2

Clue: look

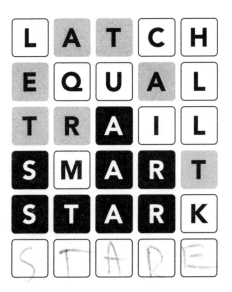

Puzzle 3

Clue: flying transport

Puzzle 4

Clue: lesson

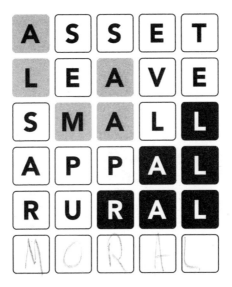

Puzzle 5

Clue: most important

G	R	E	A	T
D	R	E	S	S
B	R	E	E	D
B	R	I	E	F
C	R	I	M	E
	R	E	M	E

Q W E R T Y U I O P
A S D F G H J K L
Z X C V B N M

Puzzle 6

Clue: change

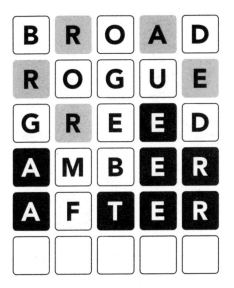

Clue: furniture

Puzzle 8

Clue: spy

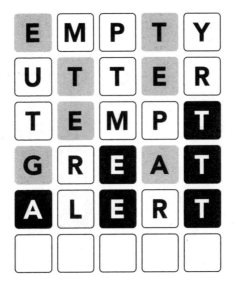

Puzzle 9

Clue: different

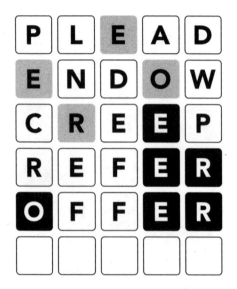

Puzzle 10

Clue: mean

Puzzle 11

Clue: open land

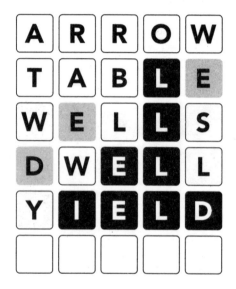

Puzzle 12

Clue: cough

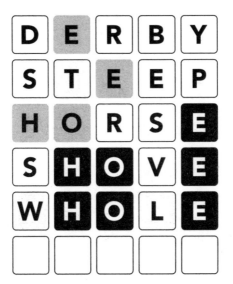

Puzzle 13

Clue: pleased

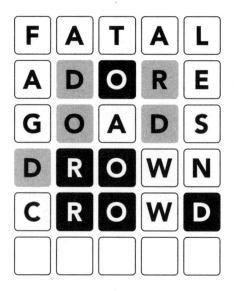

Puzzle 14

Clue: apple

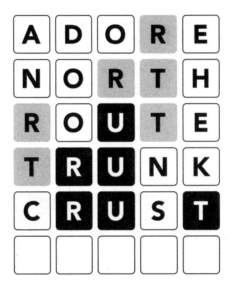

A	D	O	R	E
N	O	R	T	H
R	O	U	T	E
T	R	U	N	K
C	R	U	S	T

Puzzle 15

Clue: not better

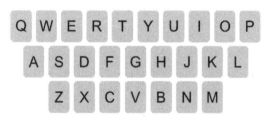

Puzzle 16

Clue: dessert sauce

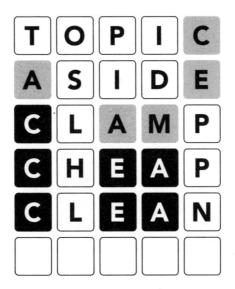

T	O	P	I	C
A	S	I	D	E
C	L	A	M	P
C	H	E	A	P
C	L	E	A	N

Q W E R T Y U I O P
A S D F G H J K L
Z X C V B N M

E
A
S
Y

Clue: place for ball games

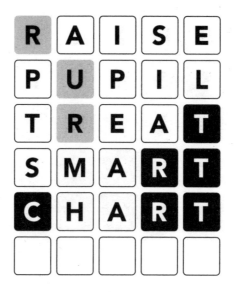

R	A	I	S	E
P	U	P	I	L
T	R	E	A	T
S	M	A	R	T
C	H	A	R	T

Q W E R T Y U I O P
A S D F G H J K L
Z X C V B N M

Clue: huge mammal

Puzzle 19

Clue: responsibility

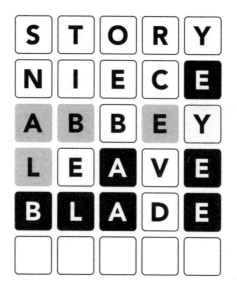

Puzzle 20

Clue: traffic light

Puzzle 21

Clue: male relative

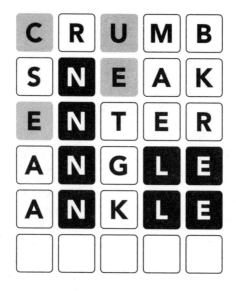

Puzzle 22

Clue: connected

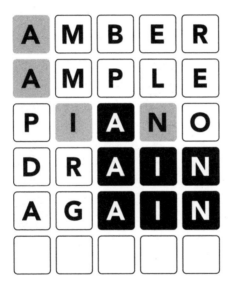

Puzzle 23

Clue: glow

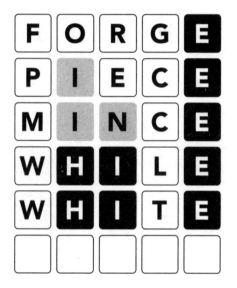

Puzzle 24

Clue: thin point

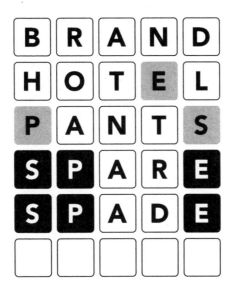

E
A
S
Y

Clue: satisfaction

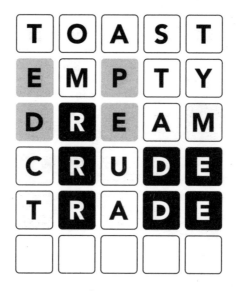

Puzzle 26

Clue: perspire

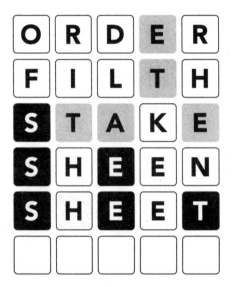

Puzzle 27

Clue: ending

Clue: tiny droplets

Puzzle 29

Clue: compose

Puzzle 30

Clue: holy person

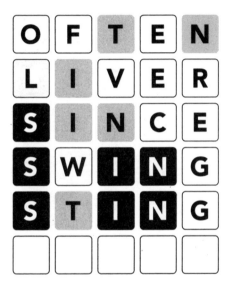

Clue: brooch

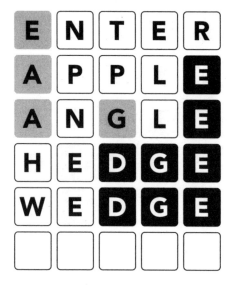

Puzzle 32

Clue: wash

E
A
S
Y

Clue: own up

T	R	U	N	K
W	R	I	S	T
T	W	I	S	T
D	E	B	I	T
L	I	M	I	T

Q W E R T Y U I O P
A S D F G H J K L
Z X C V B N M

Puzzle 34

Clue: very pale

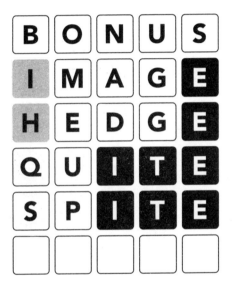

B	O	N	U	S
I	M	A	G	E
H	E	D	G	E
Q	U	I	T	E
S	P	I	T	E

Q W E R T Y U I O P

A S D F G H J K L

Z X C V B N M

Puzzle 35

Clue: hard

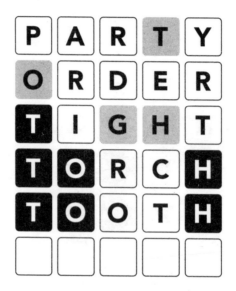

MEDIUM

PUZZLES

Puzzle 36

Clue: prepared

T	R	U	M	P
E	X	I	S	T
R	O	U	G	H
R	A	D	I	O
R	E	A	C	T

Q W E R T Y U I O P

A S D F G H J K L

Z X C V B N M

Puzzle 37

Clue: entertain

S T O C K
U P P E R
L E A R N
I S S U E
M O U S E
☐ ☐ ☐ ☐ ☐

Q W E R T Y U I O P
A S D F G H J K L
Z X C V B N M

Puzzle 38

Clue: sweet

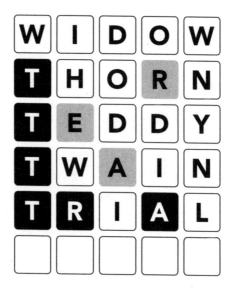

W	I	D	O	W
T	H	O	R	N
T	E	D	D	Y
T	W	A	I	N
T	R	I	A	L

Puzzle 39

Clue: number

Puzzle 40

Clue: evidence

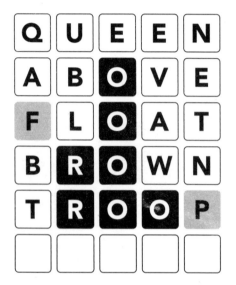

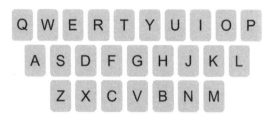

Puzzle 41

Clue: voucher

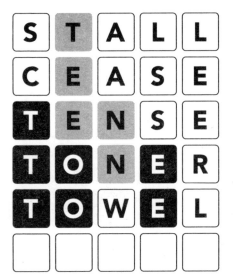

S	T	A	L	L
C	E	A	S	E
T	E	N	S	E
T	O	N	E	R
T	O	W	E	L

Puzzle 42

Clue: overflow

OCEAN
DELAY
PLUCK
CHILL
DRILL

QWERTYUIOP
ASDFGHJKL
ZXCVBNM

Puzzle 43

Clue: direction

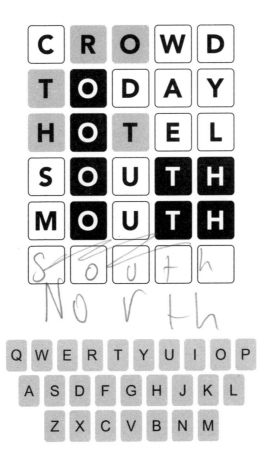

Puzzle 44

Clue: not sharp

MEDIUM

Puzzle 45

Clue: ability

H	E	D	G	E
G	L	O	A	T
T	I	T	L	E
C	H	I	L	D
S	M	I	L	E

MEDIUM

Q W E R T Y U I O P
A S D F G H J K L
Z X C V B N M

Puzzle 46

Clue: split

A	F	T	E	R
S	K	A	T	E
A	W	A	K	E
S	T	A	C	K
S	L	A	C	K

Q W E R T Y U I O P
A S D F G H J K L
Z X C V B N M

Puzzle 47

Clue: clothing

P	R	O	O	F
D	R	E	A	M
R	I	G	H	T
S	T	A	R	T
S	M	A	R	T

Q W E R T Y U I O P
A S D F G H J K L
Z X C V B N M

Clue: vegetation

Puzzle 49

Clue: strong box

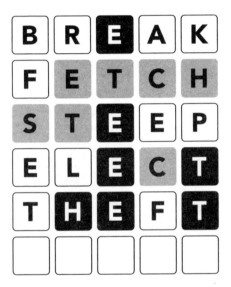

Puzzle 50

Clue: suggest

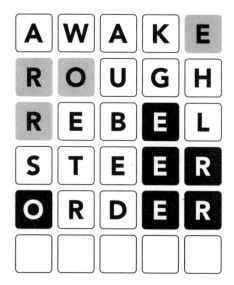

Puzzle 51

Clue: cheer

C	R	A	C	K
C	L	O	U	T
G	O	O	S	E
S	H	O	W	N
S	H	O	A	L

Puzzle 52

Clue: paper

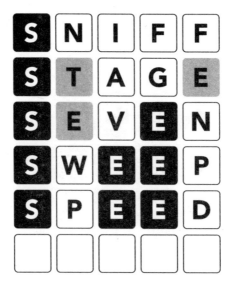

Puzzle 53

Clue: liquid

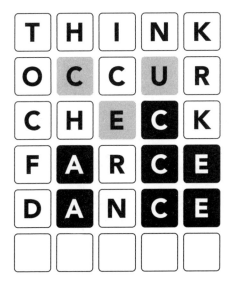

Puzzle 54

Clue: slow movement

Puzzle 55

Clue: hole

F	R	O	S	T
S	T	E	E	R
T	H	I	C	K
L	A	T	C	H
P	A	T	C	H

Q W E R T Y U I O P

A S D F G H J K L

Z X C V B N M

Puzzle 56

Clue: stay close to

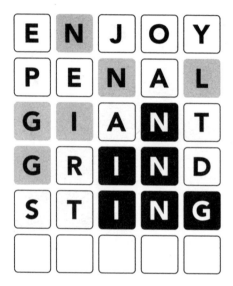

Puzzle 57

Clue: estimate

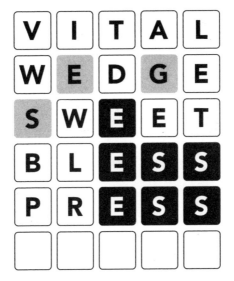

Puzzle 58

Clue: love

Puzzle 59

Clue: meal

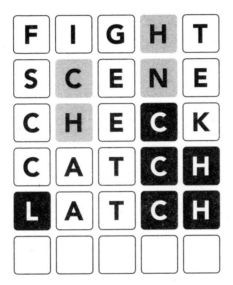

F	I	G	H	T
S	C	E	N	E
C	H	E	C	K
C	A	T	C	H
L	A	T	C	H

Q W E R T Y U I O P
A S D F G H J K L
Z X C V B N M

Puzzle 60

Clue: material for building

MEDIUM

Puzzle 61

Clue: young person

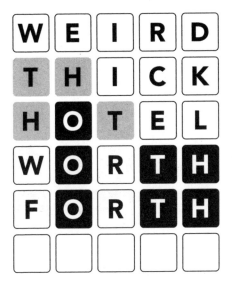

Puzzle 62

Clue: see eye to eye

C	O	U	N	T
D	R	I	N	K
S	E	R	V	E
V	E	R	G	E
T	H	R	E	E

Puzzle 63

Clue: certainly will

Puzzle 64

Clue: throw

Puzzle 65

Clue: be anxious

MEDIUM

Puzzle 66

Clue: value

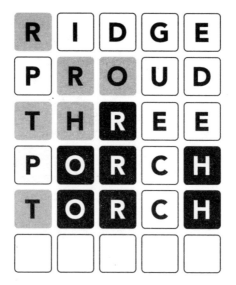

R	I	D	G	E
P	R	O	U	D
T	H	R	E	E
P	O	R	C	H
T	O	R	C	H

Q W E R T Y U I O P
A S D F G H J K L
Z X C V B N M

Puzzle 67

Clue: leader

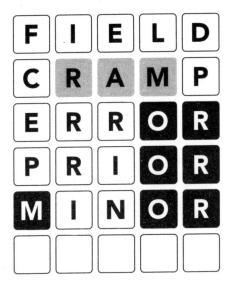

F I E L D
C R A M P
E R R O R
P R I O R
M I N O R

Puzzle 68

Clue: writing stick

B	U	L	L	Y
T	A	B	L	E
A	N	K	L	E
S	H	A	L	L
W	H	A	L	E

Q W E R T Y U I O P
A S D F G H J K L
Z X C V B N M

Puzzle 69

Clue: human body

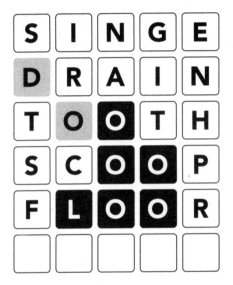

Puzzle 70

Clue: slope

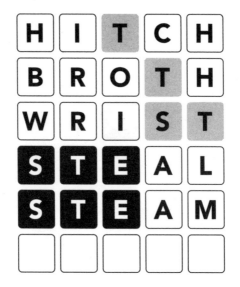

HARD

PUZZLES

Puzzle 71

Clue: all

Puzzle 72

Clue: higher

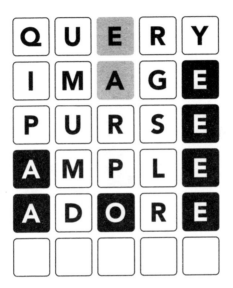

Puzzle 73

Clue: rapid

Puzzle 74

Clue: demonstrate

Puzzle 75

Clue: connection

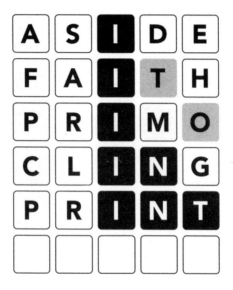

A S I D E
F A I T H
P R I M O
C L I N G
P R I N T

Q W E R T Y U I O P
A S D F G H J K L
Z X C V B N M

Puzzle 76

Clue: slow or stop

Puzzle 77

Clue: essential

Puzzle 78

Clue: cut

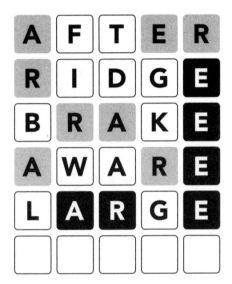

Clue: spirit

Puzzle 80

Clue: price

Puzzle 81

Clue: first thing

G	R	O	U	P
S	C	R	A	P
F	I	R	S	T
M	E	R	G	E
E	R	R	O	R

Q W E R T Y U I O P

A S D F G H J K L

Z X C V B N M

Puzzle 82

Clue: water

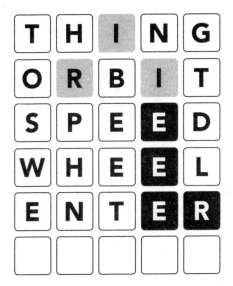

T	H	I	N	G
O	R	B	I	T
S	P	E	E	D
W	H	E	E	L
E	N	T	E	R

Q W E R T Y U I O P
A S D F G H J K L
Z X C V B N M

Puzzle 83

Clue: acceptable

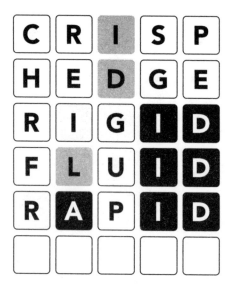

Puzzle 84

Clue: sound

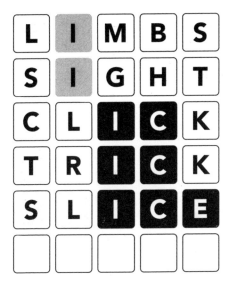

Puzzle 85

Clue: trim

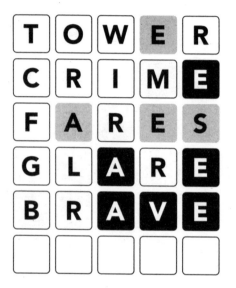

Puzzle 86

Clue: linger

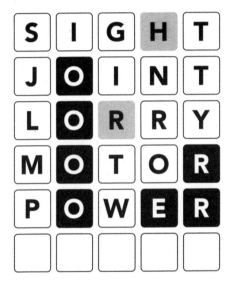

S	I	G	H	T
J	O	I	N	T
L	O	R	R	Y
M	O	T	O	R
P	O	W	E	R

Q W E R T Y U I O P
A S D F G H J K L
Z X C V B N M

Puzzle 87

Clue: feeling

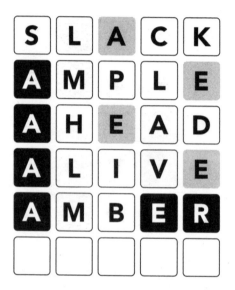

Puzzle 88

Clue: silent

HARD

Puzzle 89

Clue: cheerful

Puzzle 90

Clue: chill

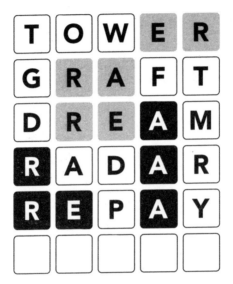

Puzzle 91

Clue: detector

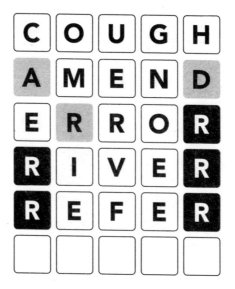

Puzzle 92

Clue: number

B E L L S
S W E A T
S C A R E
S U P E R
S T E E L
☐ ☐ ☐ ☐ ☐

Q W E R T Y U I O P
A S D F G H J K L
Z X C V B N M

Puzzle 93

Clue: monarch

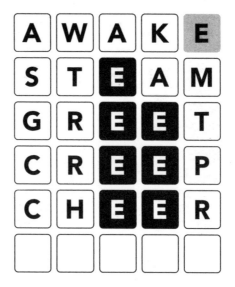

Puzzle 94

Clue: loose

W	O	R	R	Y
A	M	E	N	D
S	H	O	R	T
S	T	A	M	P
S	P	A	R	K

HARD

Q W E R T Y U I O P
A S D F G H J K L
Z X C V B N M

Puzzle 95

Clue: support

Puzzle 96

Clue: be alive

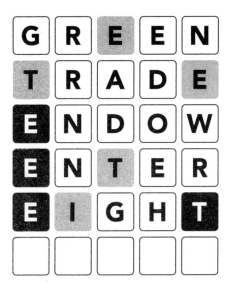

Puzzle 97

Clue: sauce

Puzzle 98

Clue: uncertainty

Puzzle 99

Clue: varnish

S	T	R	A	W
Z	O	N	E	S
C	H	A	S	E
A	W	A	R	E
F	R	A	M	E

Q W E R T Y U I O P

A S D F G H J K L

Z X C V B N M

Clue: decorate

HARD

SOLUTIONS

1: BEACH
2: STARE
3: PLANE
4: MORAL
5: PRIME
6: ALTER
7: TABLE
8: AGENT
9: OTHER
10: SPITE
11: FIELD
12: CHOKE
13: PROUD
14: FRUIT
15: WORSE
16: CREAM
17: COURT
18: WHALE
19: BLAME
20: AMBER
21: UNCLE
22: CHAIN
23: SHINE
24: SPIKE
25: PRIDE
26: SWEAT
27: FINAL
28: SPRAY
29: WRITE
30: SAINT
31: BADGE
32: CLEAN
33: ADMIT
34: WHITE

35: TOUGH
36: READY
37: AMUSE
38: TREAT
39: THREE
40: PROOF
41: TOKEN
42: SPILL
43: NORTH
44: BLUNT
45: SKILL
46: CRACK
47: SKIRT
48: GRASS
49: CHEST
50: OFFER
51: WHOOP
52: SHEET
53: SAUCE
54: DRIFT
55: DITCH
56: CLING
57: GUESS
58: ADORE
59: LUNCH
60: BLOCK
61: YOUTH
62: AGREE
63: SHALL
64: CHUCK
65: WORRY
66: WORTH
67: MAYOR
68: CHALK

69: BLOOD
70: STEEP
71: EVERY
72: ABOVE
73: QUICK
74: PROVE
75: JOINT
76: BRAKE
77: VITAL
78: CARVE
79: GHOST
80: VALUE
81: EARLY
82: RIVER
83: VALID
84: VOICE
85: SHAVE
86: HOVER
87: ANGER
88: QUIET
89: JOLLY
90: RELAX
91: RADAR
92: SEVEN
93: QUEEN
94: SLACK
95: CARRY
96: EXIST
97: GRAVY
98: QUERY
99: GLAZE
100: DRESS